Shine, Star, Shine!

YJF   18/06/22

Shine, Star, Shine!
Published in Great Britain in 2021 by Graffeg Limited.

Written by Dom Conlon copyright © 2021.
Illustrated by Anastasia Izlesou copyright © 2021.
Designed and produced by Graffeg copyright © 2021.

Graffeg, 24 Stradey Park Business Centre,
Mwrwg Road, Llangennech, Llanelli,
Carmarthenshire, SA14 8YP, Wales, UK.
Tel: 01554 824000. www.graffeg.com.

The publisher acknowledges the financial support
of the Books Council of Wales. www.gwales.com

ISBN 9781914079238

1 2 3 4 5 6 7 8 9

Shine, Star, Shine!

Dom Conlon

Illustrations Anastasia Izlesou

GRAFFEG

Open your eyes!

Someone shook a fizzy universe
and a festival of colour sprayed out.

It's a nebula – gas and dust
squeezed 'til it sparks
and this is how our Star is born.

Some stars are big, some stars are small,
some blaze blue with great heat,
but all of them forge the stuff in their hearts
to make trillions of planets and moons.

Our star's called the Sun
and without her there'd be
no life on this planet called Earth.

Let's open the curtains and let the light in and

shine, Star, shine!

Star rises in the east to bring out the day
turning the dark sky to gold.

Look, here comes a stag, the crowned king of morning,
here comes a jackdaw, clattering a warning
and here comes a fox who's red as day's dawning.

We live and we play, we work and we sleep
and Star's at the heart of it all.

In one turn of the Earth there is night and there's day
as it orbits the star we call 'sun'.

That orbit's a loop around Star's blazing sphere
bringing spring, summer, autumn and winter.

When an eagle owl sleeps, it's time for others to wake so
shine, Star, shine!

Star ripens the wheat on Idaho farms
adds fire to spice in Punjab,
and the flowers and forests from China to Brazil
grow wild on all of her strength.

But Star does much more and her light rushes on,
so let's see where else she is felt.

Here in Californian, whale-blue waters,
children play in the heat of Star's gaze.

They are light-sponges, wave-dancers, sand-stormers
having such fun in the sun.

But Star can burn too and do so much harm
so there's cream to be used as a shield.

Now follow her light from the east to the west and
shine, Star, shine!

Quick as a switch Star reaches the ocean,
pumping air from floating green gardens.

Then she lifts up the wind
and heats up the water,
which cools into clouds high above.

But whilst rainbows show off her colourful coat
she's more than a welcoming sight.

She's a world-burner, planet-turner
so shine, but don't shine too bright.

Here in the desert, some creatures stay quiet
and others emerge in the night.

Water is scarce but Star doesn't stop
so leap on a sunbeam and

shine, Star, shine.

North Pole and South Pole, each ice-capped cold snow-bowl,
why do you stay frozen through?

In summer Star stays low
in winter she's mostly below.
This leaves the poles cold, as snow reflects heat
whilst the light shimmers eerie and blue.

Above the North Pole
are an aurora of wings
rippling on the Earth's atmosphere.

Let's turn the page over and turn the light on

and shine, Star, shine!

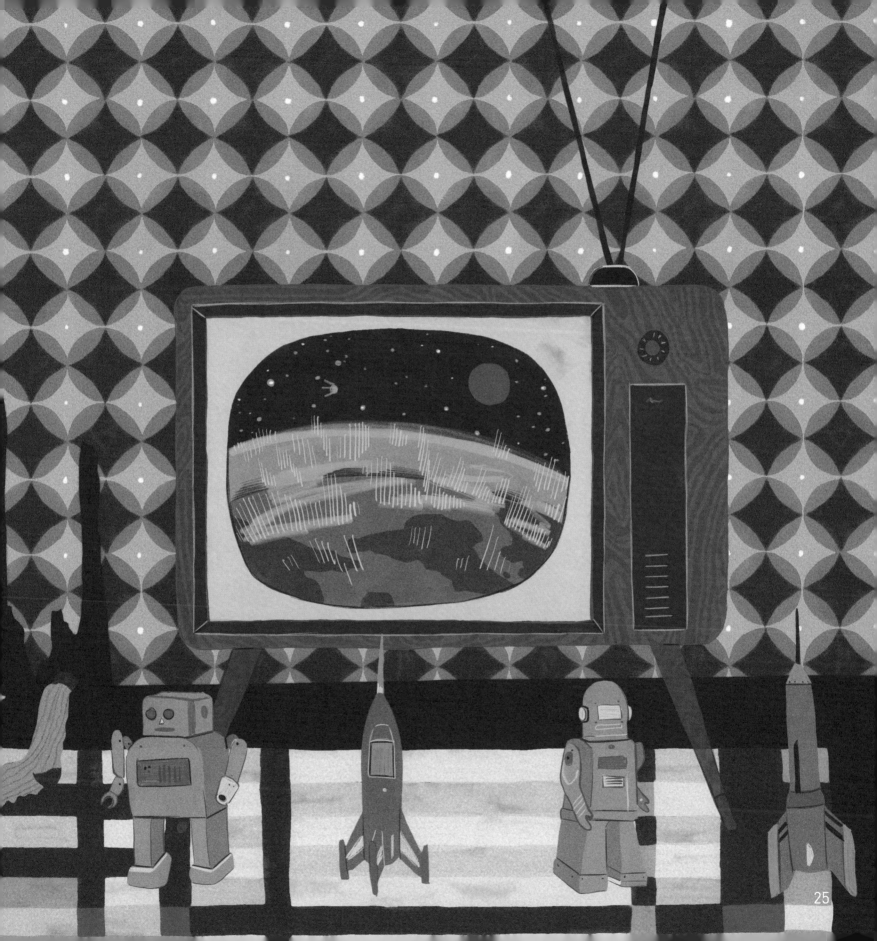

Shine, Star, shine, all through the days,
through seasons, through years and through lifetimes.

Earth keeps on turning, and night-time
and snow start to fall.

Curtains will close but there's just time to peep
at the brothers and sisters of Star.

Draw lines dot-to-dot to make hunters and bears,
to make queens and serpents and more.

There are trillions of stars with planets of their own
whose stories are yet to be heard,

so close those eyes, dream stars of your own and

sleep, Star, sleep!

Star Facts

This book shows the good and bad things our Star (which we call the Sun) does between sunrise and sunset. Some ideas and words might be new to you. Here are some explanations.

Nebula – A nebula is an enormous cloud of gas and dust which gathers together and becomes really tightly packed. Squeezing something tightly makes it hot, and if there's enough gas and dust then it will burst into flame and turn into a star.

Dot-to-dot – We call patterns made from stars in the sky constellations. There are 88 constellations, and some famous ones include Orion (a hunter), Cassiopeia (a queen), Draco (a serpent) and Ursa Major (a bear).

Planet – The world we live on is a planet called Earth. There are eight planets moving around (or orbiting) our star.

Rainbow – When light from our star shines through the rain it bounces out in different directions, splitting white light into all the colours we call a rainbow.

World-burner – Planets like Mercury and Venus are very close to our star and are very hot.

Planet-turner – Because the Sun (our closest star) is so big, it has a strong force called gravity which keeps the other planets in our galaxy spinning around it. All objects have this force, but the Sun's is much stronger.

Floating green gardens – Most of the air we breathe on Earth comes from ocean plant life called algae.

Dry – Parts of this world become very dry and are called DESERTS. The world's hottest Desert is the Lut desert in Iran, but a desert can also be very cold – Antarctica is the biggest desert on Earth.

Frozen – The ice caps stay frozen because the Earth is tilted. That means the Sun doesn't get very high in the sky even in summer, and so doesn't heat the land or sea very much.

Solar power – It is possible to collect the energy coming from the Sun and use it to power things on Earth. The International Space Station, 220 miles above Earth, has large panels which also collect solar power.

Aurora – The ripples seen from space (and they can be seen from Earth too) are called aurora. They're caused by parts of the sun's energy entering our atmosphere.

Day – A day is the time it takes the Earth to turn once, giving us daytime and night-time, but did you know that the first countries to see sunrise each day are Samoa during autumn and winter and New Zealand during spring and summer? Both are in the Southern Hempishere.

Dom Conlon

Dom Conlon is a double Carnegie-nominated poet and author whose work is guided by nature and the stars. He's written poetry and picture books, fact and fiction – sometimes all in the same book.

Nicola Davies said *Leap, Hare, Leap!* is 'full of the lushness of summer'. Chris Riddell said *This Rock That Rock* contained 'words and pictures that are quite simply out of this world'. Dallas Campbell said *Meet Matilda Rocket Builder* is 'a must read for all aspiring rocket scientists'.

Dom hopes to inspire everyone to read and write poetry. Discover more at www.domconlon.com.

Anastasia Izlesou

Anastasia Izlesou is an illustrator and graphic designer based in the UK.

Her work is full of bold natural elements and celebrates movement and shapes. Anastasia draws inspiration from her research and a wide variety of interests, which include the natural sciences, folklore and everyday objects.

Anastasia Izlesou was nominated for the Kate Greenaway Medal for *Leap, Hare, Leap!*, published by Graffeg.

You can find more of her work at www.izlesou.co.uk.